Going to the Dog

Therapy Stories For Grown-Ups

by PAUL DE MIELCHE

With

PICTURES BY CATHY MALKASIAN

PAW PRINT
Beverly Hills, Ca. 90212

GOING TO THE DOG

THERAPY STORIES FOR GROWN-UPS

With Dr. Whiskers

by **PAUL DE MIELCHE**

With

PICTURES BY CATHY MALKASIAN

"Going To The Dog"

Therapy Stories for Grown-ups, with Dr. Whiskers.

by

Paul de Mielche, Ph.D.

with

Illustrations by Cathy Malkasian

Published by Paw Print Publishing Company
   420 South Beverly Drive
   Suite 208
   Beverly Hills, Ca. 90212-4411 U.S.A.

"GOING TO THE DOG";
"Sessions with Dr. Whiskers,
"Walter Won't Eat Ants", and Other Stories."
A creation of Paul de Mielche.

Written by Paul de Mielche and
Illustrated by Cathy Malkasian.

Copyright 1994; Paul de Mielche
Text; Paul de Mielche.
Illustrations: Cathy Malkasian.
Registered; all rights reserved.

Printed in The United States of America

Library of Congress Cataloging in Publication Data.
de Mielche, Paul/ Malkasian, Cathy
"Going To The Dog"; Therapy Stories For Grown-ups, with Dr. Whiskers.
1. Self-help.
2. Psychology.
3. Animal Stories.
4. Relationship therapy.
5. Short Stories, fiction.
SAN 297-9543
ISBN 1-883785-02-2 14.95
$14.95 Soft cover.

Appreciations.

Special thanks go to Betty, Sue, Anita and Doris for their encouragement and support, and to Lucky for patient wisdom in the advice department.

Table of Contents

INTRODUCTION

FORWARD, by Author.

Dr. Whiskers, the wise old mixed-breed DOG, was invented little by little, story by story, as a way to help my therapy clients gain insight and objectivity into their behavioral and emotional problems. Dr. Whiskers' therapy stories involved animal patients, whom, they would discover to be quite similar to themselves or the people they were having trouble relating to. Breakthrough insights were often obtained in a subtle non-threatening manner.

A story can slip past the defensive obstacles to change, amusing the conscious mind as it drifts easily into the subconscious where it can do its therapeutic work. We all grew up with anthropomorphic animal stories and the little insights to behavior and morals that they revealed. It's a familiar arena in which we feel comfortable. We do our best learning in comfort, when we are relaxed.

Amazingly, Dr. Whiskers took on a personality and voice of his own. His wisdom comes from a wonderful creative subterranean world of myth and folklore, drawn from long forgotten Danish children's books that were read to me by my father and grandfather when I was a child. I have them to thank, just as Dr. Whiskers, himself, will thank the professional "Uncles" who have added to the wealth of written material that all psychologists have at hand to guide them in their search to understand human behavior.

The eight patients in these stories make up the four basic personality types, their typical relationships, behavioral attitudes, and problems. My contribution ends here. The voice you will hear from here on is that of the little Doctor with the wagging tail. A first reading will give insight. One of the characters will be uniquely like you. A second reading will reveal a familiarity and tolerance of the other characters who aren't like you. Their behavior won't seem quite so strange. We are not all the same. Read aloud, the stories are even more therapeutic; they will profoundly influence your behavior.

The wonderful illustrations of the gifted Cathy Malkasian enhance the sense experience and make the idea of a memorable story book for grown-ups aesthetically complete.

Paul de Mielche

PREFACE TO STORIES:

The DOG Introduces Himself.

Before I begin, let me assure you that these are true stories. All the characters are based on real patients of mine. Their names haven't been changed, because their behavior isn't so much different than that of others of their type, and they have done nothing more unusual than be themselves.

I write this book with their permission, that you may gain from it the insight that they have gained from our sessions together.

I'd also like to say, for the record, that no Dog stands alone. Generations of Dogs before me added to the wealth of Mammal guesswork that was passed on to me when I was just a pup. My special approach to being a Dog rose out of the discovery that so many different applications and theories of Mammal Behavior seemed to work. It is the nature of a pup to ask why. The answers I received from my many qualified and respected Uncles, Aunts and Cousins taught me that there can be as many approaches and solutions to a problem as a pup has relatives.

Experience has helped me to select the more appropriate approach to each patient, depending not upon a rigid methodology, but upon the character traits and comfort needs of the Mammal involved.

Let me single out for special thanks those grand Dogs who taught me the most important lessons:

Great Uncle Sigmund Airedale revealed that there can be a vast difference between what we "think" we want to do or should do, and what our "instincts" make us want to do; that each of us is a four legged conflict of interests.

Uncle Alfred Sheep dog helped me to look at an individual according to his social needs, his feelings of superiority or inadequacy in relation to his peers and to the whole of his environment, not just the color of his fur. He asked, "Where are we comfortable and with whom?"

Uncle B.F. Doberman's training revealed how much we can learn through repeated tasks, and how important the quest for rewards and the avoidance of pain is to every feeling creature. He taught me that the body and emotions have a memory of their own.

Cousin Fritz Terrier taught me to shift the emphasis away from, "Why do we have a certain problem?" to "How can we solve it?".

Uncle Wilhelm Spaniel emphasized the powerful implications of the sexual drive, resulting in either frustration or fulfillment; their echoes reverberating through our senses of Self. His cousin, William Cocker, elaborated on these theories by showing that there are varieties of degree in need and urge, and that they influence other behaviors as well.

Uncle Carl Basset stressed the value of letting the patient's own natural qualities emerge to help himself, the value of listening, and the notion that the less advice given, the more likely it will be carried out.

Uncle Carl, C.G. Hound, opened up the world of symbols and helped me look for the common bonds in instinct and arch-typical mysteries that we all share as Mammals, that make it possible for those of us who are Dogs to be able to sympathize and give guidance to those of you who aren't.

Cousin Abraham Beagle had a lot to say about things that make us different, from the point of view of our priorities and our needs for achievement. He taught me to look for the unique differences in my patients and point them out to them so they could appreciate themselves.

My favorite Uncle, Milton Dalmatian, used stories to teach what he knew. Stories that helped me to learn that any process we follow to help ourselves will probably work, as long as we follow the process; stories that made me aware of the way we can capsulate many hours of experience into a metaphor that may save someone else from having to go through the same experiences. Stories that made me realize that each of us makes up his or her lives as we go along and can be influenced for the better by the happy ending stories of others.

I've learned from my years of seeing patients and telling them stories about one another (being careful, of course, to be discreet) that the closer the subject of a story resembles yourself the more benefit you may find in the story. I hope you will grow to love my patients as I do, and learn from their trials and triumphs that there is more than one way to skin a banana. Please feel free to enjoy them as much as I do.

Dr. Whiskers, D.O.G.

WANDA WANTS TO BE WANTED

WANDA
HIPPOPOTOMUS

CHAPTER ONE

Wanda Wants To Be Wanted

There are many reasons for going to a Dog. WANDA HIPPOPOTAMUS, for example, comes to *dump* her feelings.

"It's quite all right," I tell her, "Get them all out." It's better that she dump them on me than her husband, Walter. Walter Anteater is quite overwhelmed by Wanda already and her periodic scoldings never produce the desired result.

Wanda's biggest complaint is Walter's insensitivity to her needs. *He doesn't listen. He isn't affectionate. He never gives her compliments. He doesn't understand her.*

I never interrupt her. I just nod my head and think of the many times I've explained to her that Walter's needs aren't as strong as hers. For him, the fulfillment of her needs is a task more gigantic than the climbing of Everest. He just hangs his snoot and mumbles "I'm sorry, Dear.", his attention wandering to those little numbers in his ledger at the office. Did they tally today?

Walter is an accountant and figures that don't tally are much easier for him to deal with than Wanda's needs.

Now don't get Wanda wrong. She's devoted to Walter; always embarrassing him by telling him how cute and sexy he is, trying to anticipate wishes that he never has, quite willing to smother him with sexual affection. But she is easily hurt when he doesn't respond as she would. Walter is rarely in the mood for love. He isn't naturally affectionate. He has difficulty in expressing love to her. To Wanda, you can never give or get too much love and affection.

When Wanda first came to see me she and Walter had been living together for three years. She had quit her job as a waitress to devote herself *full time* to him. Now she wanted to get married and have children. But, the more she wanted commitment from Walter, the more he thought things were fine just the way they were. "Honey, let's not rush things," he'd tell her.

"Rush things!" she complained. "The man is driving me absolutely crazy. He takes me for granted. How long does he think I'm going to wait around for him to make up his mind? Doesn't he know what a wonderful woman he has? I keep telling him how much he's frustrating me and he just sits there and doesn't say a thing. How can he just sit there and not say anything? Doesn't he know how that makes me feel?"

She was definitely not hiding the fact that Walter's inability to commit was making her feel terrible.

"I expect that by now you're feeling rejected and unloved," I told her. She responded with huge Hippopotamus tears. "I've tried everything. How can I make him want me?"

I explained to Wanda that it seemed apparent that Walter doesn't thrive on emotions, as she does, her heart on her sleeve. When a generous outgoing woman like Wanda is paired with a shy introspective man like Walter it's likely that they will have this kind of situation.

She's always ready to respond to positive stimulations, her ears tuned for compliments or expressions of appreciation and love. She works hard for the kind of attention she craves, often giving much more than she gets. Her needs are so strong that if the expected compliments aren't forthcoming, she tries all the harder, and the more she needs them. The more she craves of his attention, the more dramatic she gets, and the more he withdraws. The result is that her emotional disappointments build up; a tremendous weight of unfulfilled expectations.

"You're so right," she cried. "It gets so distressful, I begin to feel heavy and ugly, so taken for granted. Finally, I get angry. The only way to feel better is to get it off my chest."

"Yes, you blow up, don't you, and tell him every little thing that he's done wrong?"

"I give him a piece of my mind, I do, I do! I get so fed up, I could just scream. He never takes me out anymore. Never tells me what he wants for dinner. I have to plan every meal and when I ask him how he likes it, he looks at his plate, like he's only just noticed it and says, "Just fine." Always, "Just fine."

" I'm telling you the man's driving me nuts!"

"You're responsive to your environment," I told her. "Your man Walter isn't. He's a little afraid of it. He's not as comfortable in the world as you are. He needs you to interpret the world for him, to help him make up his mind about things."

"He does?"
"Most definitely."

It was plain to see that what was bothering her most of all was Walter's lack of commitment. I had to help her realize what a hard time Walter has making up his mind.

"I know you're impatient," I told her, "But the problem is, Walter gets anxious at the thought of change. He doesn't know what it will bring. So, he likes things the way they are. If you want to get married, this is what you must do. Don't wait for him to propose. You plan it out, just like you do those wonderful dinners, and then tell him exactly what is going to happen, and he'll say, "Fine, just fine." like he always does. If there's a plan he'll follow it."

"But I want him to <u>want</u> to get married as much as I do! I want <u>him</u> to do all the planning for a change."

"I know you do, Wanda. But, in doing so, you're constructing a formula for being disappointed."

If you project an image in your mind of how you would like something to happen, or someone to behave, and then try to make everything come out that way, you'll guarantee disappointment. And you'll continue to be disappointed as long as reality doesn't match that mental picture. Every time you think of what you want, you'll end up with a very unhappy, frustrated feeling.

A formula for being happy in a given situation is to construct an image of what is possible for YOU to do.

"It's possible for you to plan the wedding, isn't it?"

"Yes."

"Then, why not make *that* possibility happen? If that's what you want. And don't bother yourself so much with why it doesn't happen a different way."

Wanda had unloaded all her bad feelings about the situation with Walter, so she was receptive to this new idea. I encouraged her enthusiasm in planning the wedding, and sure enough, since there wasn't any pressure to initiate anything, Walter went along. It was a big noisy wedding. Walter would probably have preferred a quiet trip to City Hall, but Wanda was so happy with the event that Walter was grateful for a chance to make her happy. He didn't have to do anything. Just show up.

So, Wanda comes once a week and dumps her feelings. I listen. I sympathize. I nod, and smile, and encourage her to praise herself for all the little things she's done during the week that escaped the attention of those she did them for. Once relieved of her burden, she lets me remind her that though Walter and the two children may not have vocalized their appreciation of the many things she does for them, they respond by feeling good, almost as good as she does doing them. This makes her happy again. She knows she has a place to dump those built-up disappointments.

Sometimes when we have a little extra time we work on noticing the little non-verbal ways people have of showing appreciation. But deep down, we both know that she would rather have her praises sung than watch for wagging tails.

Wanda can't stop being Wanda. If only her friends and family knew how to give her what she needs. A few little compliments, a thank you, or a token of their appreciation would make her glow with happiness. What is often so hard for them to give is so easy for her to receive, because *Wanda wants to be wanted.*

Going to the Dog

WALTER WON'T EAT ANTS

**WALTER
ANTEATER**

CHAPTER TWO

Walter Won't Eat Ants

WALTER didn't come to see me until a few months after he and Wanda were married. He seemed ill at ease. "I'm Walter Anteater," he mumbled, "Wanda says I never talk." He sat there, eyes downcast, as if that was all he had to say. His slumped body told me the rest of the story. He really didn't want to be there in my office. He had come because Wanda had laid down the law and forced him to do something about what she perceived as his "depressions."

"He just comes home and sits," she told me. "Nothing I do seems to make him happy."

"Why don't we begin by getting more relaxed, Walter," I suggested, "And then I'll ask you a few routine questions and see if there's anything we can help you with."

I got him into a more comfortable position, asked him to close his eyes, and take some nice deep breaths; letting the air out slowly. This released some of his anxiety.

With more soothing words I eased him into a light hypnotic trance. Now he would be able to talk a little more freely; the trance state bypasses the critical part of the mind and opens the way to the subconscious.

Walter's manner of introducing himself had already told me a lot about his problem. His pronunciation of his name was mumbled with such lack of confidence that a self-esteem problem seemed evident. I made a note of that and began asking general questions about his daily life. He told me about his job as Accountant for a manufacturing company owned by Edward Lion and Allan Bear. There was an attitude in his comments of being under-valued. As long as the bills got paid and the invoices got out on time, no one respected Walter's concerns about whether the books were balanced "to-the-penny"; a subject of great pride to Walter.

When I asked Walter about his family, I learned that, while on a picnic when he was three years old, his parents were killed in a freak accident involving a runaway Elephant rickshaw. He had blocked out most of the memory of the horrible tragedy.

In a child's voice he told me, "They were having dessert. Ants and honey. Their snoots were so deep in the anthole that they didn't see it coming down the hill. I won't eat ants!"

Walter was raised by two maiden aunts who, unprepared for sudden parenthood, were more fussy than affectionate. Self-conscious and shy with girls, he had few dates in High School. He met Wanda while still going to Mammal U., where he studied accounting. At first it was too good to be true, to find a woman who loved him with so much gusto. He had never really thought of himself as a sexual being. Life with Wanda exceeded his wildest expectations. But little-by-little he began to realize that along with her great ability to give came great expectations. He found himself feeling smothered, pulling away from her, unable to match her emotional needs.

Walter opened his eyes and revealed his innermost thoughts. "Sometimes I wonder," he said sadly, "if I wouldn't have been better off alone, not sharing my life with anyone. I don't feel that I have much to offer. I don't know how Wanda puts up with me?"

"Well, you certainly weren't given much preparation for relationships in your upbringing, were you?" I nodded my head so that he would agree before I continued. "You're pretty lucky to have found someone like Wanda who cares enough about making it work to overcome your fears and reservations. The problem I see, Walter, is that her style of behavior is so different from yours that it probably overloads you."

That perked his interest. He'd been ready for a session of pointing out all his drawbacks and trying to change them.

"You're an Anteater," I told him. "You come from generations of mammals who got very good at applying their attention to one thing at a time, in small morsels, which is the proper way to eat ants. Grazers have a way of going at life in big chunks, which is the way they were taught to eat for survival."

"I hate ants," said Walter. "I hate being stuck with a name that represents something that I don't do. Why couldn't I have had a classy Latin name like Hippopotamus or Rhinoceros?"

"Well, their behavior wasn't quite so specific or accurately defined as you Anteaters, so their ancestors had to resort to Latin. But, tell me, Walter, why is it you don't like ants? Is it because your parents died while distracted by the pleasures of ant eating? Is there a part of you that's trying to protect yourself from pleasure for fear that something terrible will happen?"

"I don't know," Walter replied. "I never gave it much thought. I don't think about pleasure much." He let himself go deep into thought, searching for something he found pleasurable. I knew this wouldn't lead anywhere unless I helped it along.

"What do you think of when you think of eating ants? Is it the taste, the wiggling on your tongue or the crunchy feeling?"

"I think about when I was starting school and the other kids would tease me and yell, 'Walter eats ants, Walter eats his Aunts.' And then they'd all laugh at me."

"And when you came home your Aunts probably said, 'Eat your ants, Walter, or you won't grow up to be big and strong,' right? So, quite naturally, you rebelled against everybody and decided to stop eating ants. Who needs to be big and strong when you have so many other fine qualities."

"I do?"

"Of course. Reminds me of one of my Uncles' patients, Sherlock Anteater. Sherlock was very much like you. He liked to take things in one at a time and mull them over before making a conclusion. It took him a long time to make up his mind about things. He was having difficulty in deciding what to do about a career until Uncle Sigmond suggested that he try detective work. At that time, police work was catch as catch can. Detectives had to be strong and fast on their feet. His style of methodical detecting was based on his natural way of doing things. He taught the world that there's more to solving crimes than what first meets the eye."

Walter straightened up in his chair as he identified with the great Sherlock.

"You have that same natural talent, Walter. It comes from being an Anteater. That's why you're so good with numbers. You approach those little things one at a time until they add up to a meal, just like eating ants."

Walter brightened even more, "My word, never thought of it that way."

"And talking about words, let me share something I've learned about communicating with grazers with Latin names. They handle things in large quantities, even words. So, in cases where a few words might do, they're likely to be more generous and use too many. Your style of listening is to try to deal with each word, one at a time, and pretty soon you get lost and accused of not listening."

"You're right! That's exactly what happens. My mind just wanders off after awhile. Wanda keeps making the same point over and over."

"She needs a lot of information to understand things. She thinks everyone else is the same as she is. She needs a response. Just find a phrase that she's said and repeat it. That will tell her that you know what she's trying to say and she'll stop that particular train of thought. Otherwise she'll just keep repeating the same idea and overload you. The key to Wanda's behavior is that she keeps trying until she gets a response. Make sense?"

Walter nodded. "She keeps talking until she gets a response. I never thought of it that way." Then he smiled, "And the sooner I respond the less she'll talk. Is that what you're saying?"

"See how good you are at figuring things out?"

From that day on Walter Anteater approached life with more confidence. He knew that his approach to life was all right, that little-by-little, with understanding and patience, he could learn how to cope with his wife, just like Sherlock Anteater learned to solve his famous cases.

As Walter grew more comfortable with his true nature, he even developed a liking for ants. This was a joy to Wanda, who knew fifty ways to cook them.

Going to the Dog

ANDREA CREATES HER OWN CAGE

ANDREA TIGER

CHAPTER THREE

Andrea Creates Her Own Cage

ANDREA TIGER commands the room when she enters my office. Her appearance is always immaculate. Dressed in the latest fashion from her chain of chic clothing stores, Andrea will move about the room, circling the chairs, trying to make up her mind where to sit. Her whiskers are stiff, as if alert for danger. Her tail moves about, a separate entity, touching and caressing the objects around her. New environments are hostile to her until she has made them familiar.

It is always the same. Andrea selects a chair and makes small talk, as if she hardly knows me, until she is comfortable. With her tail up, moving this way and that, like a cobra, she takes a scented handkerchief from her purse and cleans the dust from my tea cart. She rearranges the cups, and then folds her paws in her lap. This is the signal that we can now begin to talk about her reason for coming.

Little by little, as we talk, her tail will sink to the floor and curl protectively around her chair. It's a beautiful tail and sometimes it communicates more effectively then she does.

"I know I'm supposed to be working on self-criticism, Dr. Whiskers," she'll tell me, "But..."

Very critical of others, Andrea is even more critical of herself. "I'm always on my case, Doctor," she told me on her first visit. "How can I expect excellence from others if I'm not excellent enough?" This constant striving for perfection causes endless troubles with her employees, who feel that nothing they do will ever please her.

In our initial explorations together, Andrea and I discovered that the root of her obsessive perfectionist behavior is a strong fear of being out of control. As a cub she had been rambunctious and uninhibited, a constant embarrassment to her mother. There were numerous incidents, common to tiger kittens who are learning to control their instincts. She playfully pounced on the Mail-Bird. The Mouse who did her mother's nails refused to make house calls after Andrea chased his tail.

She was constantly getting her claws caught in the lamp cords, toppling the lamps and breaking the bulbs. Her mother told her that if she continued to behave like an unacceptable "wild" animal, "I'll have you caged!"

There is nothing more frightening to a tiger than the thought of being "caged." Andrea worked hard at controlling her wild "instincts" inhibiting her emotions to gain her mother's approval and acceptance.

"Curb your appetite, young Lady," her mother told her. "Don't dirty your dress." "Watch your tail!" In other words, she was told not to behave like a tiger.

When Andrea grew older her mom taught her this prayer. *"Lord, I don't ask for much, but what I get should be of very good quality."* Little Andrea said these words every night by the side of her bed, much to her mother's pleasure. Now she can smile at the memory of that prayer, but the desire for quality still remains. It is ruled by the fear of not being acceptable.

We learned during those early sessions that the critical voice in Andrea's head, that made her critical of herself and judgmental of others, was the voice of her mother. Her rigidity comes from her childhood fear of being caged and from her desire to please her mother.

As she matured, Andrea actually grew anxious if she felt her emotions being stimulated. She found solace in structured behavior and the acquisition of "quality," the stuff of her childhood prayers.

Andrea understands her behavior, now, but old defensive habits are hard to break. She still hears that critical voice and when confronted by new situations, or her own compelling desires, Andrea still protects herself by creating an imaginary cage.

We have devoted whole sessions to help Andrea get along with her employees. Andrea has a strong inner sense of how things "should be," but she is loath to verbalize her feelings. So when her "girls" take time from their duties to do their hair or talk about their boyfriends, Andrea can make them feel very uncomfortable with a flair of her nostrils or a cold stare. It's as if she thinks that they should read her mind and react accordingly. The result is that they know she is displeased, but they don't know why. Eventually they break into nervous, insecure sobs or quit with an angry outburst, *"You expect too much, Andrea!"*

"Communicate your needs," I remind her. "And respect the fact that they have different needs than you do. If they know what you expect from them, how to please you, then you'll have better results, just like your mother did with her "wild little kitten." Andrea likes that. She likes results, and this approach has improved the atmosphere in her stores considerably.

Andrea's struggle with the desire for excellence also interferes with her personal relationships. Currently she is having an on-again-off-again relationship with Allan Bear. Allan is her ex-husband, Edward Lion's, partner. An artist, Allan has a more casual approach to life than she does.

Andrea proclaims indifference to Allan, telling herself that he possesses very few of the qualities that she expects from a man. He isn't well groomed. His hair is unruly. He wears the same mis-matched shirts and pants that he wore in art school. She hates to be seen with him in public. And though his business is flourishing, Allan has no interest in the quality life to which she has aspired.

Andrea doesn't understand why she puts up with Allan, barely tolerating him at times, she's always on the lookout for his faults. Why, she asks, does she let Allan succeed in his attempts to make her "purr"? When he does, she further surprises herself by becoming wild and passionate. And then she hates herself in the morning.

"You're in conflict with yourself," I tell her, "You can't ignore the strong needs you have for physical stimulation. When you continually deny your emotions your body rebels and decides to have a party."

"Oh, Doctor," she says, "Let's not be vulgar. I can't stand it when I behave that way." But her tail betrays her, curling up over the chair to stroke her arm affectionately in remembrance of what a good time she had.

"Andrea," I remind her, "You are very sensitive to physical stimulation. It's important for you to have an emotional outlet with someone you can trust. Allan Bear isn't a threat to you. He cares for you very much. You don't have to put up that defensive cage with Allan.

"I certainly couldn't trust Edward, that's for sure."

"Exactly, and though there were many things you admired about Ed Lion from the standpoint of ambition and success, his vanity and philandering left you wanting emotionally."

"That Son of a Bitch!" Her tail began to twitch and beat the soft arm of the chair.

"Allan brings out softer qualities that you've repressed so long that you're afraid of them. And he isn't critical. You could use a little time away from that critical voice you carry around."

"But, Dr. Whiskers, I don't know if I can respect a man if he isn't critical."

"I'm not critical."

"But you're a DOG."

"It's just a title, not to be taken too seriously. Now I want to run a pretend experiment with you. Picture yourself as a little tiger kitten whose worst fear has come to pass. Picture her locked in a cage."

Andrea clutched her paws to her chest and wound her tail around herself as if imprisoned, so strong was her imagination.

"Now, let's pretend that someone who cares about you, someone for whom freedom is very important, comes and lets you out of the cage and tells you that when he is with you you'll never have to be caged again."

The tail unwound and the paws pushed out as if swinging wide the cage door. Andrea stretched out her arms and smiled.

"Are you suggesting that Allan is going to deliver me from my worst fears?"

"I'm saying that if you can respect his loyalty and kindness, and appreciate his ability to melt that cage you protect yourself with, you'll learn that you have choices. You can choose when you want to use the cage and when you don't. This will give you more control, not less. You might even learn how to let that little kitten, in you, have a good time without feeling guilty."

The tail began to sway to and fro, in carefree abandon, revealing her inner thoughts. "I'd like that," she said.

ALLAN IS ANXIOUS TO PLEASE

ALLAN BEAR

CHAPTER FOUR

Allan Is Anxious To Please.

ALLAN BEAR comes from an easy-going, affectionate family of small brown Honeybears. Always positive, Allan had been taught to approach the world with a trusting innocence. His father was a "non-aggressive," an advocate of the Peace Bear movement that his generation of Bears cultivated to undo the fierce "Grizzly" image of previous generations. Allan looked at life with joyful curiosity and enthusiasm. But, as with many naturally optimistic creatures, Allan was totally unprepared for a more negative, skeptical view of the world.

Confused by his floundering relationship with Andrea Tiger, Allan became vulnerable to her critical, "nothing and no one is good enough for me", attitude. The more he tried to please her the more things she found to criticize. He began to have doubts about himself. No longer trusting his own instincts about his talents and self worth, he began consulting others about his "*faults*".

"What are the flaws that keep Andrea from loving me?" he asked his friends. They generously added more negative traits to his growing list. Everything he previously accepted as attributes were now considered as defects. He became self-conscious of every action, feeling more and more awkward, and less and less confident. The result was total emotional and creative paralysis.

Edward Lion wasn't helping the situation. He and Allan have a prosperous business, marketing a line of dolls based upon a popular cartoon strip that Allan once drew for their college paper. Seeing his partner stuck in the mire of low self-esteem taxed Edward's patience. He was expecting Allan to design a new ad campaign, and Allan's creative imput was blocked by indecision and introspection. Edward blamed it all on Andrea.

"She's a ball buster, Allan," Edward kept telling him. "Don't let her boss you around. She despises weakness."

This only made matters worse. Allan had reached the point where he couldn't feel good about himself without either Edward's or Andrea's approval. If he tried to do things Andrea's way to please her, he felt that he was somehow letting his friend Edward down. He remembered Edward's words and felt like a "wimp." What to do?

Heather Lamb, Edward's sweet new young wife, tried to help by taking Allan to a Psychic Turtle. Seth Turtle gave Allan his stock words of wisdom. He warned Allan that without some basic changes in his lifestyle, his past would become his future. This generally harmless advice about the need to change and adapt added more negative thoughts to Allan's confused state of mind. He had always believed that his childhood had been happy. But now he mistrusted the way he was raised. Is that where the "flaws" were nurtured?

Worried now about the past, Allan sought the help of a Spiritualist Owl; Melba, the trance channel. She called forth Allan's maternal grandmother, Granny bear, from eternal hibernation.

"You were a sweet little cub, always doodling and having fun," said Granny's voice from Melba's beak. "The only complaint I ever heard from your Mom was that you were always starting new projects and never finishing the old ones. She was always after you to clean up your room."

Allan left the seance thinking of himself as a "messy" slob, a procrastinator, feeling so low about himself that he made an appointment with me.

"I have serious problems," Allan told me. "I don't know if you can help me."

"I'm sure I can," I reassured him. "Tell me about them." It took less than an hour of questions and answers for me to understand that his "problems" were rooted in compounded suggestibility to criticism.

"I can't seem to please anyone, anymore, Dr. Whiskers. There are so many things that I need to change about myself that I don't know where to start."

"Well, let's start by talking about what you mean by pleasing others. It sounds to me like you've been focusing on all the ways you can't please them, instead of the ways that you can. That's no fun."

Allan's big brown eyes blinked back a tear as he remembered that he hadn't had fun in a long time.

"How'd you please your Granny when you were little?"

Allan thought for a moment and then smiled, "I'd sing her a song I made up about how I loved the smell of her cookies. Or I'd draw a picture of her baking."

"That sounds like fun. Did she like that?"

"Sure, she had my drawings hung up all over the kitchen."

"And how did she please you?"

Allan smacked his lips as he remembered. "She'd give me a cookie. Or two, or three."

Now that he had a more positive image of the past locked in his mind, I pointed out how they'd worked out a pretty good system, each doing things that they were good at, to please the other. Then we explored how this could work in Allan's present situation.

"You and Edward Lion didn't become partners because you admired one another's expertise at relationships, did you?

"Hardly," Allan laughed. "We were roommates in College. Whenever we needed money for rent, I'd draw some pictures and Ed would sell them."

"Now that sounds like a nice system. You do something you're good at, and he does something that he's good at, just like you did with your grandmother. So, what's a guaranteed way to please Edward?"

Allan thought for a moment. "Well, I guess he'd be real happy if I thought up a new product line for him to manufacture."

"Would it please you if he sponsored the research or market testing?"

"Why sure."

"Feels good if you can please others by doing what comes easy for you, doesn't it?"

"You make it sound simple."

"It is. But you have to remember a few simple rules. Never ask your friends for criticism. And if you need advice, ask for positive advice from an expert. For example, what can you expect when you ask Edward for advice about Andrea? He's got no more insight into her behavior than he had when they were married. They are both very opinionated and assertive. Their relationship didn't work out because he wasn't flexible and understanding, like you."

"You think so?"

"I know it for a fact."

"You have a lot of special qualities, Allan, that you've been neglecting in your search for flaws. I think it's time to use your talent for tolerance to accept that Andrea is a fussy, overly-critical personality type. Let her know that you understand that, and that you can live with it because of your easy-going nature. She'll appreciate it, because this was something that Edward couldn't do."

We explored the attractions that drew Allan and Andrea together in the first place. I taught him how to help her to recognize them and appreciate them.

"This will give you your confidence back and she'll appreciate you even more."

Allan agreed that what he had lost in the relationship was confidence. I asked him to think about times that he had pleased her. He remembered stroking her tail 'til she purred.

"Good. Now I'm going to tell you a way that you can thwart some of her criticism and give her a way to please you, as well."

Allan listened intently.

"Ask her to help you re-design your wardrobe."

He thought about my suggestion for a moment and then smiled.

"Positive advice from an expert."

"Exactly."

A few weeks later Allan sent me a couple of drawings depicting the results of the work I had done with him. They featured Allan and Andrea, paw in paw. He was dressed in his new wardrobe, looking very spiffy and confident. Andrea looked proud of her renovative work on his appearance. Needless to say, I was pleased.

Sybil Can't Find Her Feelings

SYBIL FOX

CHAPTER FIVE

Sybil Can't Find Her Feelings.

SYBIL FOX always has cold paws. When she visits, I seat her near the fireplace and wait while she quietly holds all four paws out to the flames.

"I can't ever get them warm enough," she tells me. "If I had it to do over again, I'd have married a guy with fur instead of a thick-skinned Rhinoceros."

Sybil is married to Al Rhinoceros, a salesman who works for Edward Lion and Allan Bear. They met at Mammal College. She was a law student and he was on a football scholarship. Sybil was a shy little thing, an honor student devoted to her studies. She had never really thought of herself as attractive until she met Al, the gregarious popular campus hero. All the girls were after him, but he pursued the only coed who didn't seem to know that he existed. Overwhelmed by his persistence, she gave in and became, in every sense of the word, HIS.

A knee injury forced Al off the football line. So, as far as he was concerned, there was no reason to continue going to school. He quit in his senior year and went into sales so that he could afford to marry Sybil. Sales suited him. He moved from one job to another and received top commissions everywhere he worked. There was no financial need for Sybil to quit school, so Al "generously" allowed her to pursue her degree. It made him feel good to tell his friends that his little Fox was studying law.

Al didn't really think that Sybil would practice law after she passed her Exam. After all, he was making lots of money. He was looking forward to making babies and raising a family. Her decision to pursue her law career made him very unhappy. Al began to realize that Sybil's ideas of being a wife were different from his expectations. She was pursuing a career because she wanted to, not because he was letting her. From that point on their marriage became a contest of wills: Al wanting more from her; Sybil giving less.

Now, a good many years later, there are still no babies. Sybil and Al sleep in separate bedrooms, both putting off talking about separation. She can't face an emotional confrontation with Al. He can't bear the thought of losing her.

So, instead of the unpleasant drama of confrontation, Sybil accepts the daily ordeal of Al's hurt feelings and disappointments. He firmly believes that he has been wronged and tries in every way to make her feel guilty. When he isn't wallowing in self-pity, his tone toward her is critical and judgmental.

"I don't feel anything anymore, Dr. Whiskers," she tells me. "Just numb. I can't give him what he wants, and I don't want to. I just want to be left alone."

Sybil never voices a specific reason for coming to see me. Maybe it's just to warm her paws, or maybe it's because she knows that I understand her. "The reason you bury your feelings," I once told her, "is because you're very delicate emotionally, and a little goes a long way with you. You're like the music lover with sensitive ears who can't stand it loud, so she sits further away from the orchestra."

"Orchestra? I married the brass band!"

The time had come for Sybil to contemplate making changes. I told her about my ancestor who was so insecure that whenever he was given a good bone he would bury it, saving it for a special occasion when he might "really need it." He buried so many bones that he forgot where most of them were, and if on occasion one got dug up it was a dirty, putrid disappointment.

"What's the point, Doc?"

"You haven't lost your feelings, Sybil. You buried them, and now you're afraid of what you'll find if you dig them up."

"I'll feel worse than I do now, is that what you think?"

"Not what I think. What you think."

We explored some of the feelings she'd find if she found some. There was sorrow because she couldn't be the way Al wanted her to be. There was pity for Al, because he'd become so pathetic in putting up with her coldness toward him. There was anger at him for being so selfish in his expectations of her. And there was guilt because she'd been having an affair with Al's boss, Edward Lion.

"Those are all feelings related to Al and his feelings," I pointed out. Maybe it was necessary to bury those. They're unpleasant. But what about yourself? What about some feelings related to you?"

Sybil thought and thought, then shook her head. She couldn't find any. "I don't know how I feel."

I reached over and held her paws between mine. "Warm?" I asked.

She nodded.

"Then think about that feeling and see if you can feel warm all over."

She sat silently with closed eyes. And then finally nodded. These were the kind of feelings she liked. Quiet ones.

I reached over and pulled one of my home-grown roses from the vase near her chair. "Smell this," I asked. "What does it make you think of."

"I love roses," she said. "Now, after our talk, it makes me think of myself. Very delicate, but thorny so you'll keep your distance. Look, but don't touch."

"How does it feel to be so delicate a rose?"

"You bruise at the slightest touch," she whispered, as if to herself. "It's a bit scary."

Sybil opened her eyes, wide. She'd learned something about herself. A feeling she'd buried. The feeling of being scared. A feeling that Big Al Rhinoceros had protected her from, until his emotional demands overwhelmed her and made her withdraw into herself again.

"Oh, wow, so that's why I don't leave him. I'm scared."

"Probably not. More like scared of being scared. You're not the fragile little flower that you were when you first met Al. You've worked hard to be independent. Self-sufficiency is your branch of thorns. You have nothing to be scared of anymore."

I put the rose back in the vase and looked her right in the eyes so that she would take what I said seriously. If she didn't change this situation soon her numbness of feelings would grow worse.

"Sybil, the confrontation you've been avoiding having with Al, isn't necessary. The only purpose served would be to make one of you angry enough to leave, and anger is not a good emotion for either of you to have to feel. I want you to accept that despite your independence and legal wisdom, you're up against something that neither of you can handle by your-selves. It's been going on too long."

"I want you to tell Al that you're going to move in with a girl friend for a while. Before he starts to rant and rave, tell him that I want him to come and talk to me while you're gone."

"You're not going to tell him about Edward, are you?"

"Of course not. That would only hurt his feelings all the more. It's nothing serious, is it?"

"Not at all. Edward's nice and furry. Nothing more."

It was the first time I'd ever seen her express a noticeable spontaneous emotion. She blushed. "Sometimes I get a little frisky, and you know Edward, he's always available for that sort of thing, and I don't have to worry about him making any emotional demands on me."

I couldn't hold back a chuckle. That rascal Edward. I knew it wouldn't be long before his wife, Heather, would be in to see me about his philandering.

My final words were meant to reassure her. I'm not here to make value judgments about my clients' behavior, but to guide them towards healthy changes.

"I'm going to talk to Al about the raising and care of roses, Sybil. I'm going to tell him that if they're too delicate and prickly for him to handle, not to blame the plant, but to consider a hardier type of flower. He can always sell the house and get a place where he can grow geraniums. They thrive better with heavy handling."

"Are you telling me to leave him?"

"Just a period of separation. I can't promise anything beyond that. How does that make you feel?"

"Relieved."

And that's how she felt when she left my office. Relief. It was a start.

Big Al Sings The Blues

BIG AL RHINOCEROS

CHAPTER SIX

Big Al Sings The Blues.

An angry Rhinoceros can be quite intimidating. So So when AL RHINOCEROS rang me up for an appointment a few days after I had seen his wife, Sybil, I sent Maria Squirrel, my housekeeper, out to do the grocery shopping. Al was snorting when he entered the room. I was tempted to move behind my largest easy chair until he calmed down.

"Did you tell my wife to leave me?" he demanded to know.

"Yes," I told him. "Since you both seemed to be making one another's lives miserable, I thought a period of separation might be in order." He looked like he wanted to tromp me, but he didn't move, so I continued. "And now you're even more miserable, without her, and you want her back, am I right?

He glared at me for a moment more and then sighed a deep sigh. "I miss her so bad that I ache. Tell me what to do, Doc. I can't go on this way."

He was still standing, filling up the room. I thought of asking him to sit down, but I knew that he needed to work off some more steam before we could do any serious talking. "It's my guess that you've been aching for a long time, Al. Sybil hasn't been there for you lately, has she? Physically, I mean."

"Did she tell you that?"

I nodded. "But even if she hadn't, it would have been quite obvious to me. Sexual withdrawal is quite common, you know, when one partner's emotional needs are much stronger than the other's. Sexual intimacy begins to seem like a demand, and there's a tendency to back away, to withhold affection."

"Withhold affection? She hasn't let me touch her in six months. I'd call that a pretty revolt'n development, wouldn't you?"

I risked a smile. "Revolt might be just the word for it."

"Look here. I always treated her right. Gave her everything she ever wanted. Never laid a hand on her. So don't you sit there making cracks. I know you're taking her side. But what about me? I love her and now she's walked out on me. Do you know how that makes me feel?"

"Terrible. You ache all over. We'll get to doing something about that in a moment. But first tell me, do you love her the way she is, or the way you want her to be?"

"What's the difference? I know how I feel. I don't need you to tell me how I feel. She can be any way she wants and I'd still feel the same. Even now. She knows I'm dying without her, and still she walks out on me, and I don't stop loving her. Can't you see what she's doing to me, Doc? You've got to tell her to come back. I'll do anything she asks. Just come back home." His big brown eyes were pleading with me. He wasn't angry anymore, but he was feeling extremely sorry for himself.

"You've got a fine, big, expressive voice, Al. Did you ever do any singing?"

"Singing? What the drunk giraffe has that got to do with anything?"

"Well, you're a very physical person, Al. Unlike Sybil's, your emotions are very close to the surface. The moment you feel them you have to release them, otherwise they build up and make you uncomfortable. Am I right? When you were younger, you probably released a lot of this emotional energy in sports."

He nodded proudly. "All-city tackle in High School. Got a scholarship. You could see the fear in the quarterback's eyes when I came on the field. Could have made the pros if it wasn't for this darned knee."

"Sybil's like one of those Ivy League quarterbacks who needs a lot of time to make a pass, and you're in there quick, rushing. The only way she can keep from getting sacked is to say, "No!" That stops everything, like a penalty whistle. But it's the only way she knows to keep all those emotional expectations of yours from swarming all over her. Do you understand what I'm saying?"

"I come on too strong, right? Edward's always telling me that. He sez I'm his best salesman, but sometimes I come on too strong, turn some of the customers off. I try to work on it, but it's hard, you know. You can see the sale starting to slip away and you want to reach out and grab the guy and shake some sense into him. I guess I hate to let anything go, and that goes double for my wife."

"There's a choice, isn't there? You can either change your style or accept a rejection now and then."

"There's plenty of new customers out there. They don't like me the way I am, I go some place else."

"Is that what you told Sybil?"

"I am who I am, Doc. I'd feel like a phony if I pretended to be some different kind of Rhino, you know?"

"That's sort of the way Sybil feels too, Al. I'm just repeating to you what I told her. If you can't accept the way a person is, and you can't change them, then the only thing you can change is yourself; your attitude about the situation. And if you can't change that, then you have to accept the loss."

"Don't say that, Doc. I'm already aching. How am I gonna feel if I lose her? What if she finds someone else?" He clutched his heart and moaned at the thought.

I tried to console him. I didn't want jealous fantasies to get him angry all over again. I was just getting his attention.

"I wouldn't predict anything, right now, Al. You're both just taking a break. But for your own sake, it's important to be a little more objective about the situation. And in order to do that you need to understand what causes this kind of disaffection."

"So let's say I understand. Then what?"

"Then we give you some options. For one, you need a new outlet for your emotions. That's why I suggested singing."

"Singing?"

"You'd be surprised what a physical release that can be, and, with your timbre and ease of self-expression, you might even find it socially rewarding, as well."

"I don't know, Doc. I don't exactly look like a Frankie Hyena, you know."

"I'd guess you're a baritone. Jimmy Moose was a baritone. Remember him? What was that song he made so famous." I hummed a few bars of Jimmy Moose blues and tapped my paw on the table so that Al could hear the rhythm.

Al broke into a smile and started to sing the words. *"I got the blues, from my horns to my hoofs, I feel so baaaad.."*

I jumped up. "Great! Now belt it out. Put all your emotions into it."

"AH GOT THE BLUUUES, FROM MY HORNS TO MY HOOFS, I FEEL SO BAAAAD..."

I thought the table was going to crack when he put one hoof on it and turned toward the window, singing so loud that the glass began to shudder. *"AH FEEL THE PAAAIN, FROM MY HEART TO MY BRAIN, I FEEL SO SAAAAD."*

"Sing it, Al, get those feelings out. Make them dance. Tell them who's boss!"

It was working. The more he sang, the better he felt. I could see the physical release in him, and when he was through, and sank smiling into the chair, I knew that he felt good, better than he had felt for a long time.

"I think we can work together," I told him. "You were willing to try something I suggested and you got a positive response. Now that you're more willing to trust me, I can help you do what is best for YOU. We'll explore what will make you the happiest in the long run. I know that having a family is a top priority for you. I think that's a goal worth pursuing. I don't take sides. If it turns out that that's not what Sybil wants then I'm going to do everything I can to help you find someone else who has the same needs. The only promise I want from you, now, is to keep singing. Is that a deal?"

"You're all right, Doc. Sure. I'll give it a try."

Al kept his promise and used singing as an outlet for his strong emotions. His naturally gregarious nature took a more positive turn as he learned to understand himself better.

A few months after that first session, Al was delighted to bring a new friend by to meet me, Ida Elephant. They met in a piano bar.

Ida adores Al's singing. He's very happy.

"...Ain't nooobody...can stroke my
aphro-de-siac horn...like she can..."

HEATHER DOESN'T KNOW WHETHER

HEATHER LAMB

CHAPTER SEVEN

Heather Doesn't Know Whether.

HEATHER LAMB has a hard time making decisions. This is because she is very flexible and adaptable and can see both sides to any given situation. Always positive, wishing the best for everyone, she is unwilling to alienate anyone by going against their wishes. This makes her very suggestible to the opinions of others.

Heather considers herself intuitive and spiritual. She has an innocence about her that is altogether tolerable. It is in fact very appealing, because though very pretty, she is also unassuming and appreciative. No one ever resents giving Heather advice or helping her with tasks, like balancing her checkbook, which she finds confusing.

Before consulting me, whenever Heather had a major decision to make she would take a survey of all her friends, including any "experts" they recommended. I was recommended by Wanda Hippopotamus.

Heather was having trouble deciding whether or not to marry Edward Lion. She had been working for Edward and Allan Bear as a receptionist during the time of Edward's divorce from Andrea Tiger. He had hired Heather because of her good looks and immediately began asking her out. Surprisingly, to him, she refused because she had discovered on previous jobs that "dating the boss" led to "complications."

Eventually however, Edward won her sympathy with tales of woe and abandonment by Andrea. Heather let him take her to elegant restaurants and theatrical opening nights, so as he put it, he could "regain his confidence with women." (Edward is such an operator.) But to Edward's dismay, though they became intimate, the conquest wasn't complete. Heather still continued to date Frank Afghan, her acting coach and aerobics instructor.

Edward couldn't stand the idea that Heather was so ambivalent about him; that she could continue to date Frank; that she would take Frank's advice and sometimes even quote Frank's "ridiculous pseudo-intellectual pontifications."

In sheer frustration Edward asked Heather to marry him, on condition that she give up "this acting nonsense" and devote herself to him. Frank, on the other paw, had no such commitment intentions. He simply reminded her that if she stuck with him she'd be fulfilling her artistic talents, and with luck and another year of lessons he might even be able to get her an agent.

What to do? Heather cared about both Edward and Frank. She didn't want to hurt either of their feelings. Her friends and acquaintances had mixed feelings and their advice left her even more confused. Many saw Edward for what he was: vain, pompous, egocentric, a playboy whose first wife had left him because he couldn't resist a pretty face. Others, like Wanda Hippopotamus, thought Heather should jump at the chance to marry such a handsome and successful lion as Ed.

"He's just a big pussy cat," Heather told me, "and I just adore him, sometimes, but you know, he can be just a little bit rigid. You know? Like it's not that he's that much older than me, but he can get real bossy, especially when he doesn't get his way. What do you think I should do, Dr. Whiskers? Everybody tells me something different."

I told her that when I had trouble making up my mind about something I'd usually turn it over to my sub-conscious. The sub-conscious mind has all the information and knows me better than anyone else. It usually knows what will make me the most comfortable in the long run.

"That sounds perfect. *Just ask the sub-conscious.* How do you do that?"

"Well, Heather, I call it Dream Performance. You give your sub-conscious the questions you want answered and it will usually do its best to come up with a solution while you are peacefully asleep, undistracted by conscious input or the need to pay attention to what's going on around you. And it usually does it by showing you a performance of some sort, like in a play or a movie."

"Sounds neat, how do I do it?"

Thus we began a few months of dream therapy sessions, which culminated, as you may know, with the marriage of Heather to Edward Lion.

Dream therapy involved the simple process of first getting Heather into the habit of watching and remembering her dreams every night. I did this with a few words of post-hypnotic suggestion on that first session and by asking Heather to write down everything she remembered dreaming immediately upon waking.

Once Heather was adept at remembering her dreams, we worked on creating a method of communication between her conscious mind and her sub-conscious. This involved symbols. We studied her current dreams, looking for repeated images and occurrences. These became her dream symbols. By relating them to daily events and past history we found some symbols that seemed to make sense to her in their meaning. Though Heather's dream symbols were uniquely personal, as are all of our dream symbols, hers were quite literal and fairly easy to detect. Now, we had a basis upon which to communicate with her sub-conscious.

Next, we created simple questions that she took to bed with her at night, by writing them in her dream journal just before retiring. When she awoke the next morning she would specifically examine her remembered dreams for answers to her questions. Sometimes she would discover that she had recognized an "answer" during a dream!

Soon Heather could recognize attitudes and feelings in her dreams and felt confident about her intuitive interpretations of what the dreams were telling her. It was time for the big question, *"Do I really want to marry Edward?"*

Since this was a matter for serious consideration, I suggested that Heather write the question in her dream journal for five nights straight, recording her dreams each morning upon awakening. After the fifth night we would analyze the dreams that she thought pertinent to the question.

It took only two dreams to make up Heather's mind. In the first she was attending a theatrical performance with Edward. Frank was on stage with another actress. She felt very envious of the other actress. During the performance Frank invited her to come up on the stage and play a very small part, in which she was totally overshadowed and outperformed by the other actress. She felt frightened and embarrassed. There were also feelings of jealousy each time Frank gestured or spoke to the other actress on stage. Finally, she left the stage and rejoined Edward. With Edward she felt comfortable and secure.

In the second pertinent dream Heather was at a costume party with Frank. Edward was with another woman. Heather joined Edward and his date, becoming friendly with the woman. Across the room she saw Frank with another woman and felt jealous and angry with him. She left with Edward and his date. When they were outside the date took off her mask and turned out to be Heather!

Heather's dreams informed her that she had a strong need for security and comfort. Sub-consciously, she was more emotionally secure with Edward. Frank stirred up feelings that she was uncomfortable with; jealousy and envy. Satisfied with this survey of her own information center, Heather accepted Edward's proposal with no further doubts or regrets.

Ever since learning about Edward's extra-marital fling with Sybil Fox, I had been expecting another visit from Heather. There are no secrets in the Mammal community. What surprised me when she came to see me about Edward's promiscuity was Heather's rather mild reaction. She didn't feel the jealous rage that Andrea had felt when learning about Edward's indiscretions. Instead, she was embarrassed for him, as it seemed to "take something away from his all important posture of dignity." It made him look silly in her eyes.

What really concerned Heather, now, was whether to go along with Edward's desire to be a father. She didn't really want to have children with a mate who behaved so immaturely, and there was that nagging question of security again.

"I know it's just a weakness he has, Dr. Whiskers, but if I get pregnant I don't want to have to be worrying about him leaving me for another woman. You know what I mean?"

"Absolutely," I assured her. "And since you are taking such a mature attitude about the situation, I'll tell you exactly what to do. You've heard of a pre-marital contract haven't you?"

"Sure. Edward had me sign something that said we each got to keep everything we had before we got married, if we ever split up."

How thoughtful of him.

"Well," I continued, "now your concerns are different. Tell Edward that if he wants a family, you're quite willing, assuming of course that you are. BUT, before there can be further action taken in the direction of pregnancy, there must be a pre-conceptual contract."

"What a neat idea!"

I thought so too. I expected to hear from Edward soon. Faced with the risk of losing not only his wife and family, but also his business, if he continued to indulge in assignations and indiscretions, Edward might be more than willing to discuss the subject of *"habit control."*

Going to the Dog

EDWARD THE INCORRIGIBLE

EDWARD LION

CHAPTER EIGHT

Edward, The Incorrigible.

I learned almost immediately that EDWARD LION is a formal, structured type of individual.

"I don't like to be called Ed," he told me. "All these years I've known Al Rhinoceros, since college, I've asked him to call me Edward, and he still calls me Ed. Why is that?"

We both knew that this wasn't the reason Edward had come to see me, but you can't help someone change his behavior if he doesn't want to make the change. And Edward was trying in every way he could to avoid the real issue: his one bad habit, his roving eye, his lascivious fondness for females of every species. I humored him with information. I always have plenty of theories on hand.

"Al's an informal outgoing personality type, and it's his way of putting everybody on equal footing, like letting everyone call him, Al. "

Edward has very little insight into himself, so he doesn't realize that sometimes his statements seem quite pompous.

"I'm his boss. I don't want to be on equal footing with him. I think it's just his way of showing disrespect, trying to pull me down to his level."

"Al doesn't think in terms of levels, Edward. Until we learn different, most of us think everyone would like to be treated the way we'd like to be treated. Al's not comfortable with being too formal with the folks he's dealing with. He likes to get casual and familiar as soon as possible and assumes that the same is true with you. It's his way of assuring your friendship. It's what makes him a good salesman."

Edward shook his mane, not quite willing to tolerate this. "Is that what this personality business is all about? Someone does something you don't like and then you're expected to just shrug your shoulders and say, "that's all right, they're just doing what's natural for their "type"? That's no way to run a business."

"Look at it another way, Edward. It can be very helpful to be able to predict how someone is likely to behave in a given situation. You can be awfully surprised by the responses you get if you always expect everyone to behave just like you do in a certain situation."

Edward thought this over. The idea of being able to predict responses appealed to him.

"Well, I guess you're just talking common sense, aren't you, Doctor? Pointing out the obvious, like the difference between a Lamb and a Tiger. Believe me I know the difference. I've married both."

"And, I gather you've had some experience with Foxes, Beavers and Hyenas, among others," I said pointedly.

That got him on track. "Helen Hyena. Does Heather know about her, too?"

"No, but she will soon if you don't stop taking those long lunches at the company apartment that Helen is "redecorating" for you."

"Who told you about that?"

"If you had paid attention to her personality characteristics Edward, instead of her physical qualities, you'd know that Helen is an outgoing, gregarious type, like Al and Wanda. They don't keep their emotions a secret, like you do. If they're in love they're going to tell the world. If someone breaks their heart everyone's going to hear about that, too."

That set him to thinking. There was something to be learned here.

"So, what am I supposed to do, Dr. Whiskers? You seem to understand the situation. There're all those lovely females out there, with all these different qualities. I can find something I like about each of them, but for the life of me I can't limit myself to just one."

He was telling the truth. A "habit compulsive" can never get enough of what he thinks he needs.

"The problem Edward, is that's just what you keep telling each of them that you'll do. You promised Heather fidelity when you married her. That's a pretty important commitment to make if you don't mean it."

"Yeah, I know, and now she's wanting me to sign this pre-conceptual thing that you two cooked up."

"You're asking her to make a lifelong commitment to raising a family, Edward. That's not something to be taken lightly. Don't you agree?"

"Look, Doctor. I'm a very successful man. I wouldn't let my kids want for a thing. If it's security she's worried about, I'll set up a life trust for each child. I'll put the house in her name. I'm not the sort that would let his family go without. You should see the settlement Andrea got, and she was always putting off the idea of having kids. Isn't that what marriage is all about, having kids?"

"It's also about trust and intimacy Edward. Monogamy is part of the deal, especially when there are children involved. That kind of emotional security seems to be a necessary building block if you want to guarantee a successful family relationship."

"Can't have your cake and eat it too, is that it?"

"I'm saying that if you can't be considerate of your loved one's feelings for you, sooner or later she won't have those feelings any more. If you want your marriage to last, the pre-conception contract is for your own best interests. Perhaps it will motivate you toward a change of attitude."

"You're asking a lot Doctor Whiskers. Let's say I went along with attempting some kind of "attitude change" in this department. Really tried to avoid distractions, if you know what I mean. And then someone just threw herself at me, and I just couldn't say no. What would happen then?"

Habit control offenders often want to make the therapist an accomplice or a policeman, sharing or taking responsibility for their client's actions. Edward was trying to make a deal with me. It was the only way he could allow himself to establish rapport.

"If you want to understand your behavior better in order to make some positive changes Edward, I can help you do that. I can help you get the most out of your marriage to Heather. But I won't help you pretend to be working on something that you know in your heart you don't want to do."

"That's straight. So, I'll be straight with you. I feel like we've been talking about my giving up something that I don't want to give up. I know it's supposed to be wrong, but I don't really feel that it's that wrong, and I don't want to. You know what I mean?"

I had to nod. I knew what he meant.

"I wouldn't mind learning some more about personality types, though, Doctor. Might help in designing a new marketing approach for next season. You could probably give me some tips on how you make different types do what you want. Right?"

I don't like the idea of using whatever I know about mammal behavior to exploit others, but I knew any mention of values or ethics would only get us off track again. Perhaps there would be time for that later. Edward has a very pragmatic attitude toward values and ethics: Whatever is best for Edward is the best thing to do. It would take some doing to change that. I accepted the challenge.

There are some who might accuse me of being too tolerant, but I can't resist the opportunity for an interesting character study, not because of the amoral adventures I knew Edward would share with me once we gained more rapport, but because of the confidence with which he seemed to flaunt the mores and standards of our carefully cultivated society. Edward has no sense of emotional responsibility. Because this is so hard to believe, Edward has an advantage over the rest of us. Perhaps his sexual exploits are the only connection he has with others. One he can allow himself because it is in some way connected with a reward, or with taking advantage, or perhaps a conquest. He married Heather because he couldn't have her any other way, and now he takes her for granted. I didn't admire Edward, but I was curious about him.

"Why don't you come in once a week for a chat Edward, and then we'll see where it goes from there."

"Great."

I've learned a lot about Edward during our sessions. His father was a Traveling Lion, affluent, but never home. Edward was raised by a doting mother and a pride of seven sisters. He was spoiled by females who gave him all the privileges of the male of the house and none of the responsibilities. He learned to expect everything from others while giving back very little. This may unfortunately be a secret of his success. Those of us who are more giving seem willing to go along with it.

I try to do what I can to teach Edward about the emotions of others, and how his behavior may affect their feelings. It is my hope that eventually he will learn to feel empathy. Perhaps he will develop a conscience. Heather tells me that he seems to be more considerate of her needs. But her needs are not excessive, and his attitude is still, "What she doesn't know, won't hurt her."

I really can't claim any success with Edward. I don't know whether his sessions with me are making any impression on him. He keeps trying to get me to condone his behavior by granting him the honor of being his own unique personality type. Perhaps he is, but I won't. It's a standoff.

Though he won't admit it, there have been some subtle signs of empathy. He contends that he's just sending me clients, as one businessman helping another. Perhaps it's his newly developed conscience working. He sends me the "objects of his affections" after the affairs are over. He's completely honest with them now. I've learned how to help them get over him very quickly.

Only last week there were the three Kangaroo sisters, Milly, Mariah, and Maude, a singing trio...
Well, that's another story.

"Going To The Dog" is a Paw Print Book. It was developed for publication by Mielchevaerk, Inc., Media Development Company. Production was by The Amazing Company. Additional Graphics were provided by Kathy Markbreit. Typesetting by UniScan Photographics.